2

Hands-On Piano

Kenneth Baker's
new three-book
piano course

GW00646247

Wise Publications
London/New York/Paris/Sydney/Copenhagen/Madrid

Exclusive Distributors:
Music Sales Limited
8/9 Frith Street,
London W1V 5TZ, England.
Music Sales Pty Limited
120 Rothschild Avenue,
Rosebery, NSW 2018,
Australia.

Order No. AM927553
ISBN 0-7119-4987-5
This book © Copyright 1995 by Wise Publications

Music arranged by Kenneth Baker
Music processed by MSS Studios
Book design by Studio Twenty, London
Cover photograph by George Taylor

Printed in the United Kingdom by
Printwise (Haverhill) Limited, Haverhill, Suffolk.

Your Guarantee of Quality

As publishers, we strive to produce every book to the
highest commercial standards.
The music has been freshly engraved and the book has
been carefully designed to minimise awkward page turns
and to make playing from it a real pleasure.
Particular care has been given to specifying acid-free,
neutral-sized paper made from pulps which have not
been elemental chlorine bleached. This pulp is from
farmed sustainable forests and was produced with
special regard for the environment.
Throughout, the printing and binding have been
planned to ensure a sturdy, attractive publication
which should give years of enjoyment.
If your copy fails to meet our high standards,
please inform us and we will gladly replace it.

Music Sales' complete catalogue describes thousands
of titles and is available in full colour sections by subject,
direct from Music Sales Limited.
Please state your areas of interest and send a
cheque/postal order for £1.50 for postage to:
Music Sales Limited, Newmarket Road,
Bury St. Edmunds, Suffolk IP33 3YB.

About this book

In Part Two of this course you learn more about 'triads', and begin using 'seventh' chords. You add a new key: G Major, to the keys of C Major and F Major, which you already know. You learn various new rhythmic 'styles', including an important Pop/Latin style, and several interesting 'Boogie' variations.

As before, the following advanced audio software is available to help you…
CD, **cassette** and **Midi file disk**
With any of these aids you can…
Hear how every song should be played
Play along with a full backing band

In addition, with the Midi file disk you can slow down or speed up the tracks as desired, and listen to different parts of the performance (for example, left hand alone, right hand alone, and so on). You will find these audio facilities an enormous advantage when learning to play the piano from these books.

About the audio

On each of the audios there are a number of lead-in 'clicks' (cymbal beats) at the beginning of every track in order to set the speed. There are four clicks with 4/4 Time, three clicks with 3/4 Time, and so on. On some of the tracks these lead-in clicks are followed by a short musical 'introduction' from the backing band. You start playing when you hear the solo piano on the backing track begin.

POP / LATIN STYLE

In this important, well used style, **a dotted quarter note (dotted crotchet)** is featured in the left hand pattern:-

DON'T CRY FOR ME, ARGENTINA (p. 5)

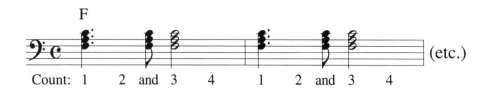

Keep your main beats (1,2,3,4) as regular as the ticking of a clock, and play your 'and' chords EXACTLY between beats 2 and 3.

KEY OF G (MAJOR)

The key of G (Major) is derived from the Scale of G (Major), which requires one sharp: F♯:-

SCALE OF G (MAJOR)

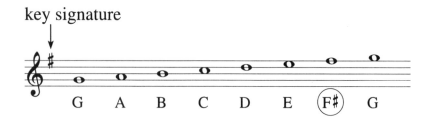

The F SHARP is indicated in the key signature at the beginning of every line, and you must remember to play every F note - wherever it occurs on the keyboard, as F SHARP.

NEW CHORD

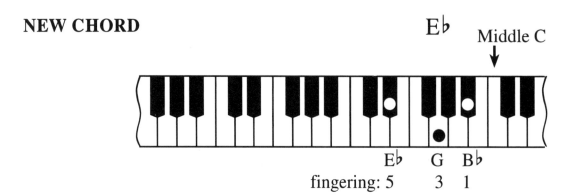

Don't Cry For Me Argentina

Music by Andrew Lloyd Webber.
Lyrics by Tim Rice

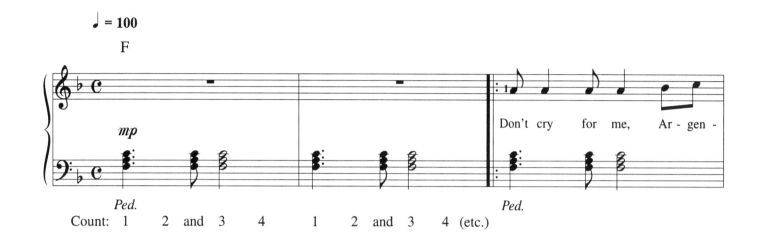

Don't cry for me, Ar- gen-

Count: 1 2 and 3 4   1 2 and 3 4 (etc.)

ti - na, ___   the truth is I ne - ver   left you.   All through my

wild days,   my mad ex - is - tence,   I kept my   pro - mise,   don't keep your

dis - tance. ___

Imagine

Words & Music by John Lennon

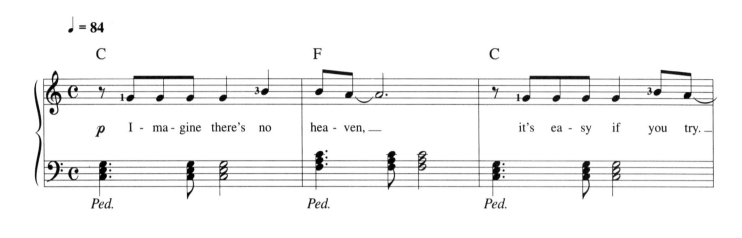

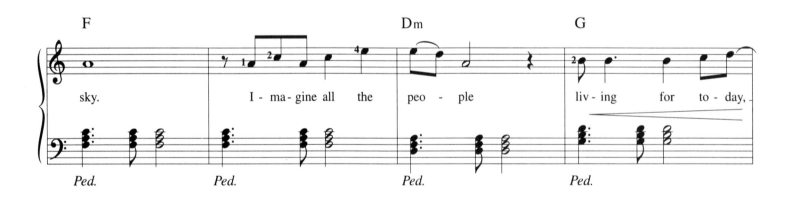

By The Time I Get To Phoenix

Words & Music by Jim Webb

9

(Everything I Do) I Do It For You

Words by Bryan Adams & Robert John 'Mutt' Lange
Music by Michael Kamen

DAL SEGNO (D.S.) AL FINE   Repeat from the SIGN: 𝄋 and continue playing until 'Fine' (the end).

11

MORE ABOUT TRIADS

The bottom note of a triad is called the ROOT e.g.:-

C MAJOR TRIAD

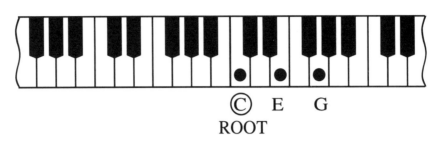

If you count up THREE letter names from the ROOT (C),
you arrive at the THIRD (E):-

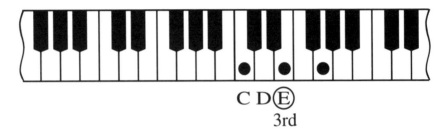

If you count up FIVE letter names from the ROOT (C),
you arrive at the FIFTH (G):-

Every triad consists of a ROOT, a 3rd, and a 5th.

MINOR TRIADS

A Minor Triad is a Major Triad with its middle note (3rd) FLATTENED
(i.e. moved one semitone to the left), e.g.:-

C MAJOR TRIAD

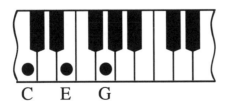

C MINOR TRIAD

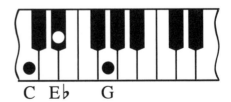

EXTENDING THE TRIAD

If you continue counting up (to the right) beyond the notes of a triad, you arrive at two other important notes: the SIXTH, and the SEVENTH, e.g.:-

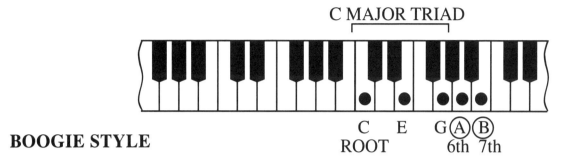

BOOGIE STYLE

This is a strong rhythmic type of accompaniment: effective, yet simple to play. The basic pattern consists of a MAJOR (or MINOR) TRIAD, with its top note (5th), moving to the 6th, or the 7th:-

example 1   YOUR CHEATIN' HEART (p. 14, bars 2 and 3)

example 2   ROCK AROUND THE CLOCK (p. 18, bars 1 and 2 of CHORUS)

In this example each of the chords is played TWICE

example 3   EVERYBODY'S TALKIN' (p. 20, bars 1 and 2)

In example 3 each of the chords is played twice, and the top note moves from the 5th, to the 6th, to the 7th, and back again.

Once established, each basic 'boogie' pattern is repeated on the other triads in the song. To keep the chord symbols simple, I have used only the basic triad names (omitting 6ths and 7ths).

NEW CHORD

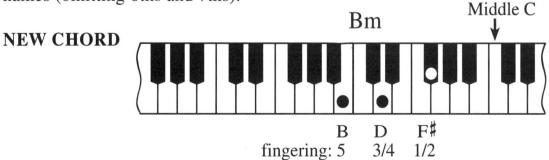

Notice the alternative fingering, 5,4,2, which might suit you better.

Your Cheatin' Heart

Words & Music by Hank Williams

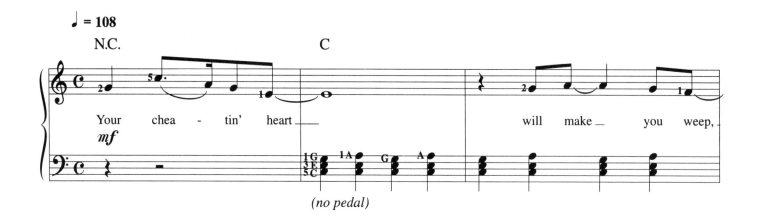

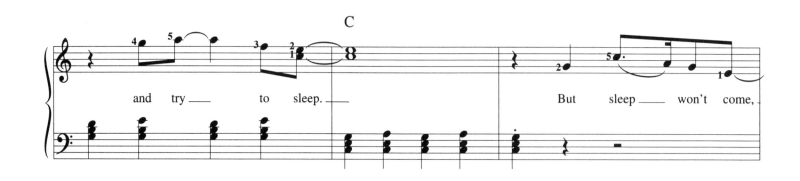

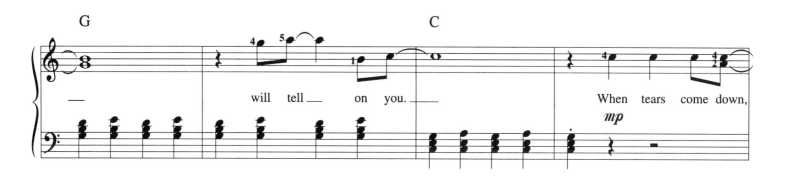

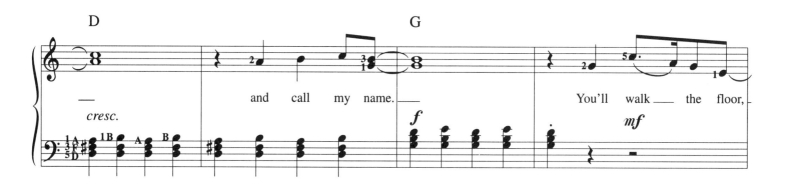

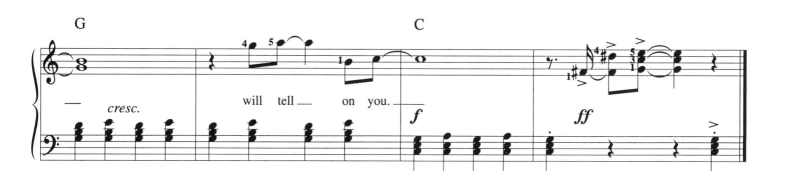

Ob-La-Di, Ob-La-Da

Words & Music by John Lennon & Paul McCartney

* GRACE NOTE. A note not included in the timing of the bar. Play your grace note(s) as quickly as possible.

Rock Around The Clock

Words & Music by Max C. Freedman & Jimmy de Knight

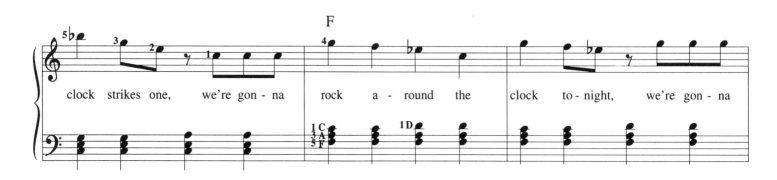

C   F

rock, rock, rock, 'til | broad day - light,   we're gon - na | rock gon - na rock a -

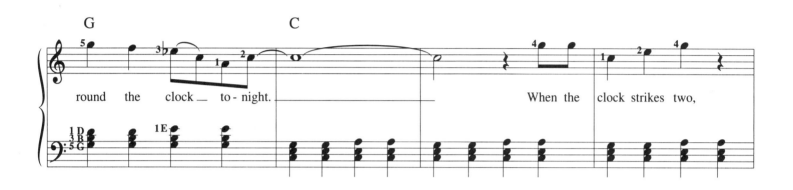

G   C

round the clock to - night.   When the | clock strikes two,

three, and four,   if the | band slows down we'll | yell for more! We're gon - na | rock a - round the

C   F

clock to - night, we're gon - na | rock, rock, rock, 'til | broad day - light, we're gon - na | rock, gon - na rock a -

G   C

round the clock to - night!

ff

Ped. ✻

Everybody's Talkin'

Words & Music by Fred Neil

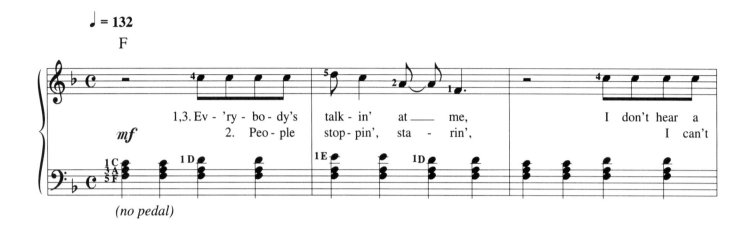

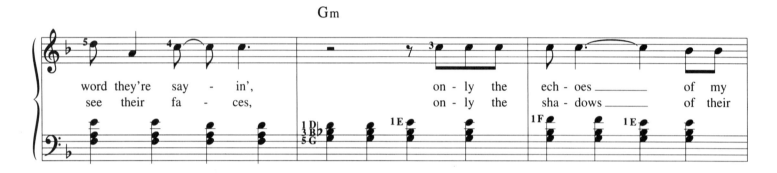

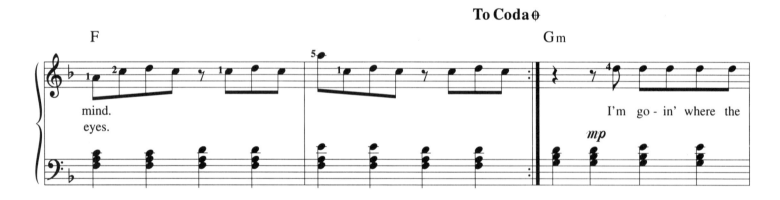

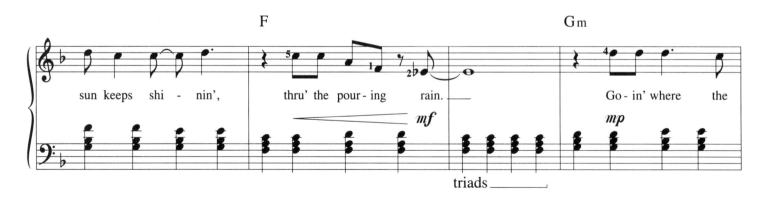

triads

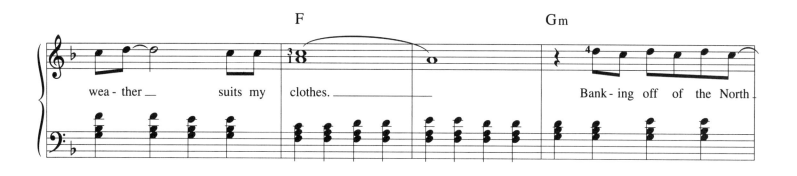

wea - ther ___ suits my clothes. ___ Bank - ing off of the North

___ East wind, ___ sail - in' on sum - mer breeze, _mf_

triads _____

and skip - pin' o - ver the o - cean, ___ like a stone.
_mp_

D.C. al Coda

Coda

Gm

I won't let ___ you leave ___
_f_

___ my love ___ be - hind. ___

(Repeat and fade)

No,

21

LOW TRIADS

When triads are played low on the piano they sound 'muddy', and rather ugly.
The simple solution is to OMIT THE MIDDLE NOTE OF THE TRIAD:-

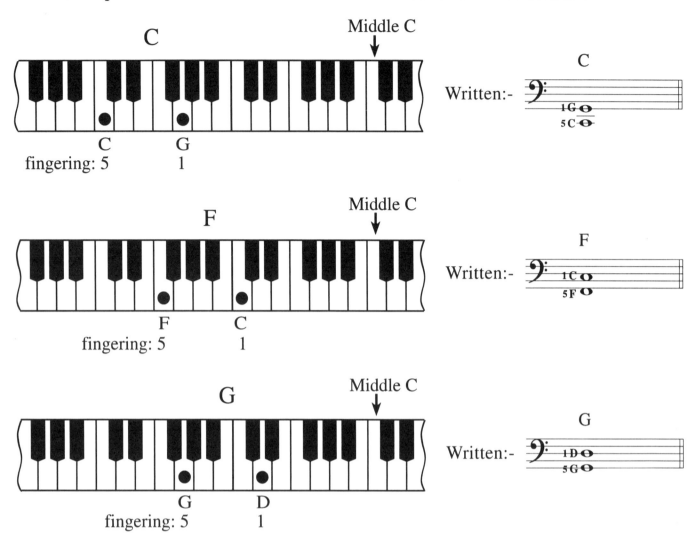

Mull Of Kintyre

Words & Music by McCartney & Laine

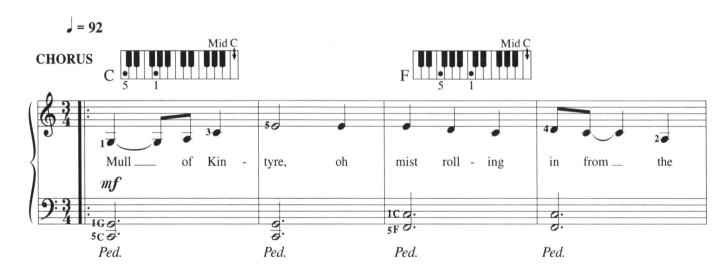

Mull ___ of Kin - tyre, oh mist roll - ing in from ___ the

Every Breath You Take

Words & Music by Sting

DAL SEGNO (D.S.) AL CODA   Repeat from the SIGN: 𝄋 and continue playing until: **To Coda** ⊕ . At this point jump to CODA, and play through to the end.

In the next two pieces the two low triad notes are played SEPARATELY.

Mamma Mia

Words & Music by Benny Andersson,
Stig Anderson & Bjorn Ulvaeus

The Entertainer

By Scott Joplin

* TENUTO. Hold this note for its full length (or a little longer).

SEVENTHS

If, on your piano keyboard, you start from a C note, and
count up SEVEN letter names, you will arrive at a B note:-

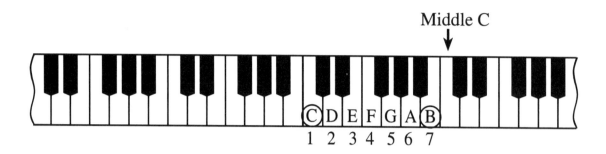

The distance from C to B is called a MAJOR SEVENTH (maj7).
If you add this B note to a C Major Triad, you form a chord called Cmaj7:-

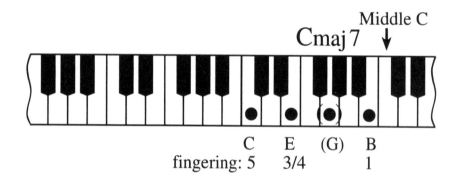

To make this chord easier to play, omit G (the 5th of the triad).

If you now FLATTEN the B note (i.e. play it one semitone to the LEFT), you
will arrive at another chord, called C DOMINANT SEVENTH - C7, for short:-

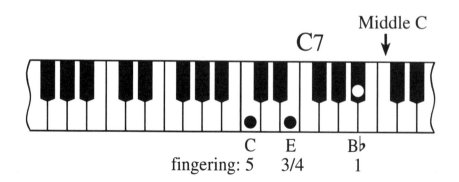

The two types of seventh note (maj7, 7) can be added to MINOR triads as well as MAJORS:-

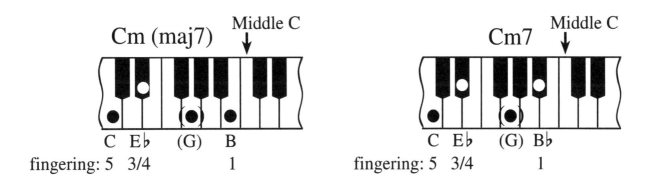

Cm (maj7)   Middle C

C E♭ (G) B
fingering: 5 3/4   1

Cm7   Middle C

C E♭ (G) B♭
fingering: 5 3/4   1

In the following pieces you will be playing a succession of seventh chords, Major and Minor, based on different roots. Point to the root of the chord required with your little finger (finger 5), and, with your 3rd (or 4th) finger and thumb, pick up the 'seventh' shape, e.g.:-

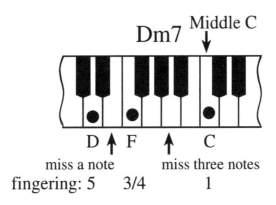

Dm7 Middle C

D ↑ F ↑ C
miss a note   miss three notes
fingering: 5   3/4   1

All the chords in these pieces consist of white notes only, with the exception of C7:-

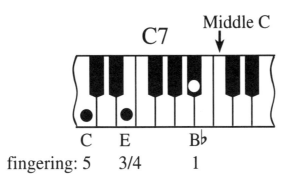

C7   Middle C

C   E   B♭
fingering: 5 3/4   1

Let It Be

Words & Music by John Lennon & Paul McCartney

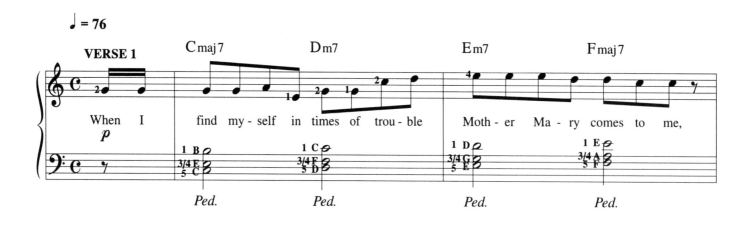

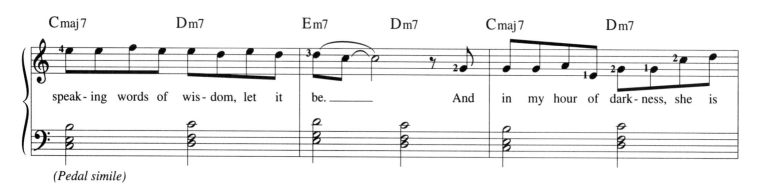

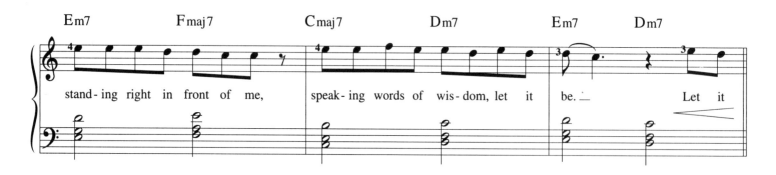

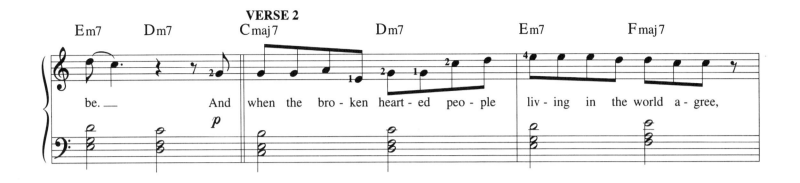

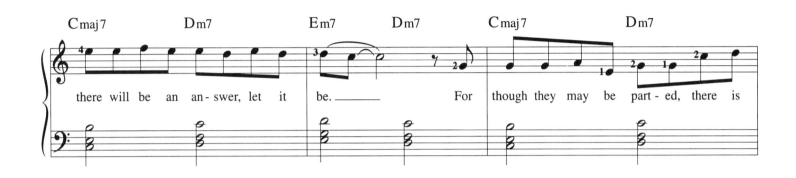

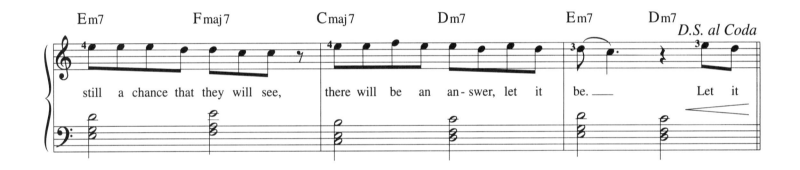

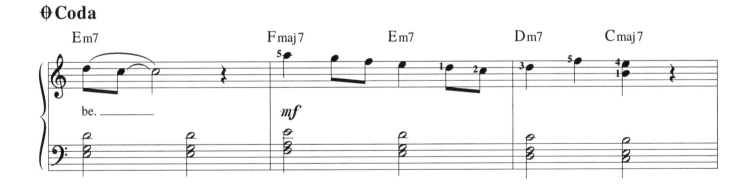

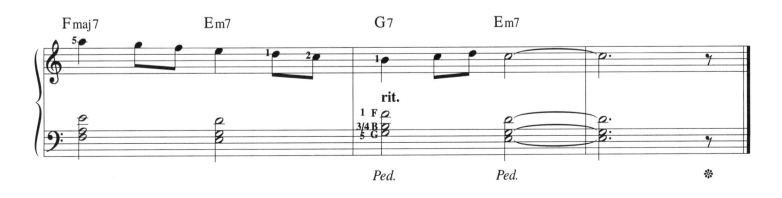

The Fifty-Ninth Street Bridge Song
(Feelin' Groovy)

Words & Music by Paul Simon

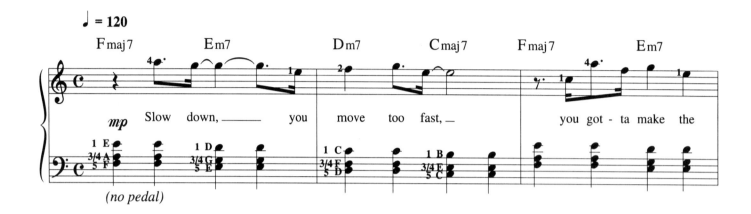

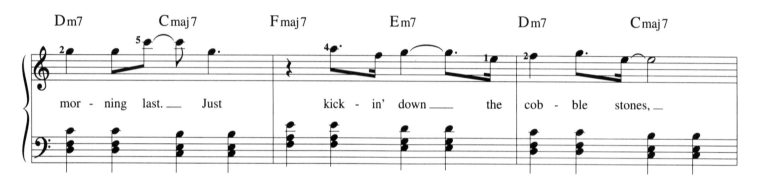

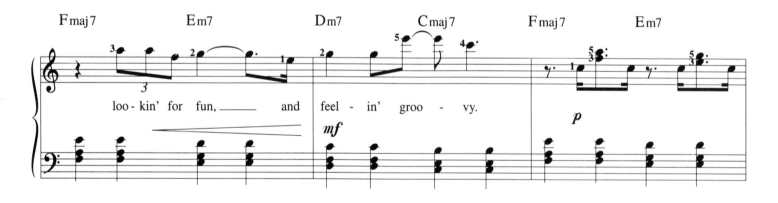

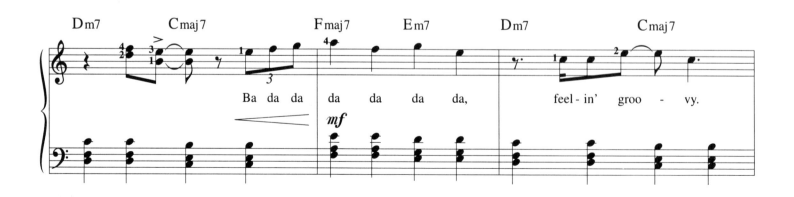

RESOLVING THE SEVENTHS

Since **seventh** chords are basically discordant, it is usually desirable to resolve them more or less straightaway:-

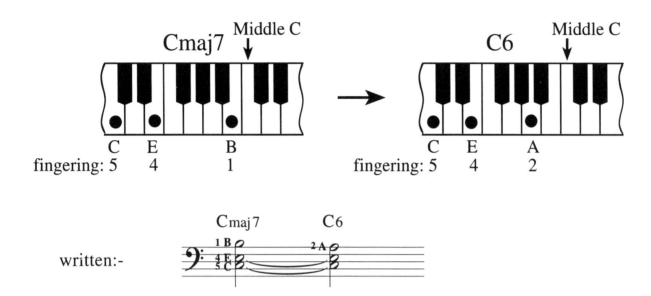

written:-

Here the **maj7** note B moves down a note to the 6th, A, resulting in a far less discordant chord C6.

Here's another example:-

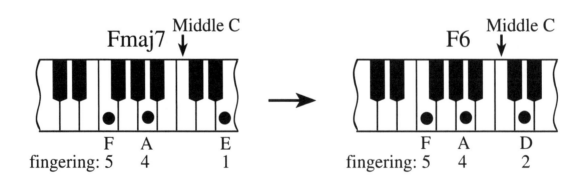

written:-

In your next few songs most of the seventh chords resolve in this way, i.e. the 7th
note (maj7, or 7) moves either one, or two semitones down to the note below.
To make these chord resolutions sound really 'musical', you should, in general,
play the second of the two chords more quietly than the first; in other words,
let the sound 'taper away' from the first chord:-

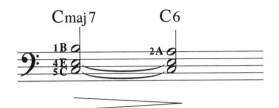

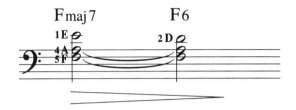

The above fingering is ideal for this sort of progression, since it keeps the top notes
legato. However, players with small hands may have to stick to a 1,3,5 fingering
throughout:-

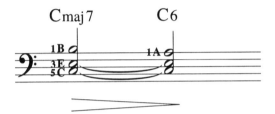

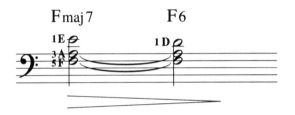

To keep the chord symbols as simple as possible, I have marked only the basic
seventh chords, followed by an (R) to indicate a resolution, where applicable.

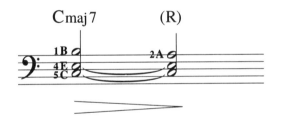

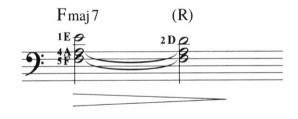

Watch your resolution notes very carefully: **they could differ by a semitone:-**

FALLING IN LOVE AGAIN (p. 41, 6 bars before the end)

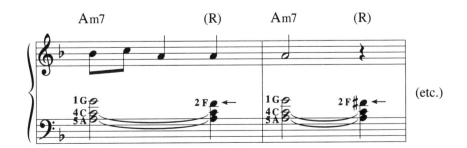

All I Ask Of You

Music by Andrew Lloyd Webber.
Lyrics by Charles Hart

Falling In Love Again

Music & Original Words by Friedrich Hollander
English Words by Reg Connelly

Have I Told You Lately

Words & Music by Van Morrison

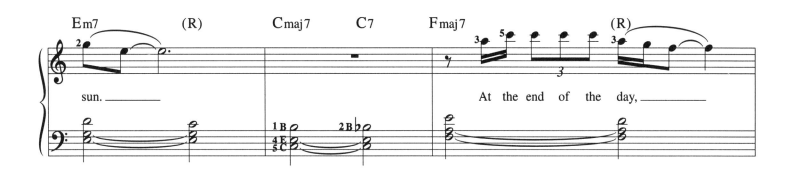

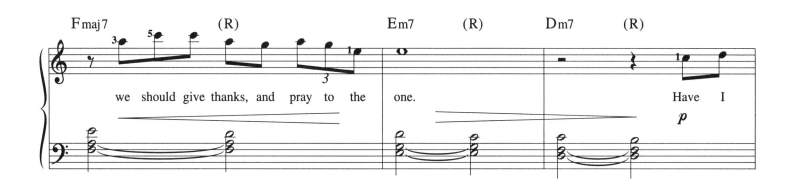

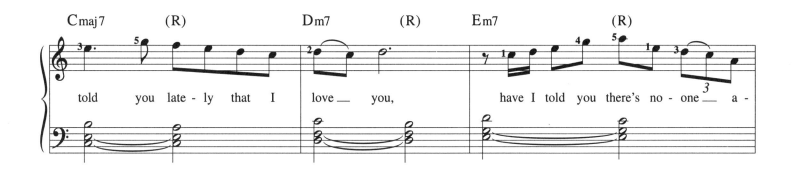

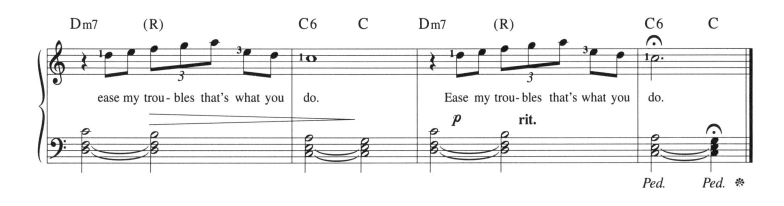

Copacabana (At The Copa)

Words & Music by Barry Manilow, Bruce Sussman & Jack Feldman

* usual Am7 chord, played one octave (eight notes) lower, for convenience.

45

CHORD CHARTS

1. TRIADS

MAJOR

WRITTEN

MINOR

WRITTEN

2. SEVENTH CHORDS, WITH THEIR RESOLUTIONS (AS USED IN THIS BOOK)

(resolution notes written small)

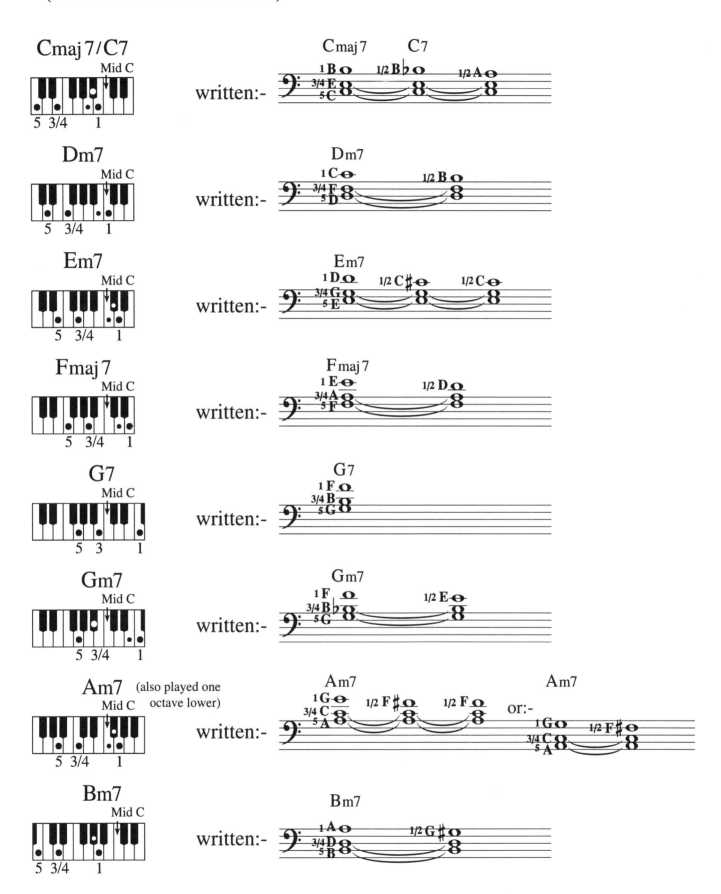

SEMITONE FORMULAE FOR TRIADS

ALL MAJOR TRIADS: ROOT → 5 → 4

examples:

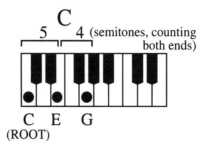

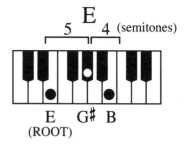

ALL MINOR TRIADS: ROOT → 4 → 5

examples:

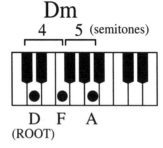

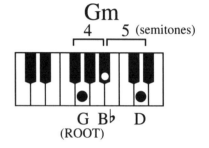

LEARNING THE WRITTEN NOTES (LEFT HAND)

While you don't need to be very fluent, a reasonable knowledge of Bass Clef will allow you to follow the internal movements of left hand chords.

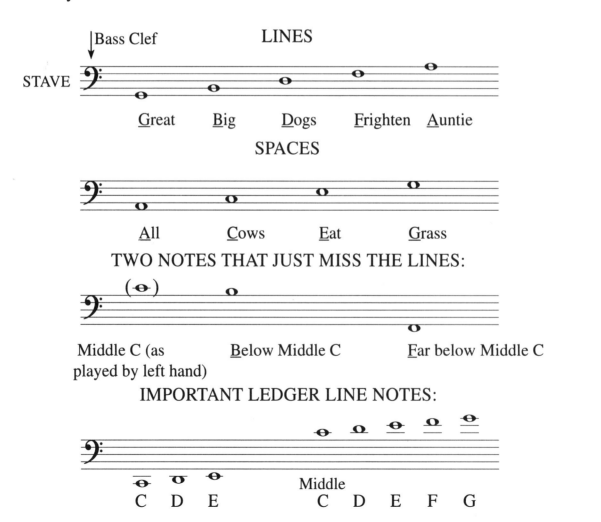

48